THE EASY PIANO SERIES

SHOWS

REALLY EASY PIANO ARRANGEMENTS
OF 12 SONGS FROM THE BIGGEST SHOWS
FOR THE GRADE 1 & 2 PIANIST

FABER ff MUSIC

BREAKING FREE
HIGH SCHOOL MUSICAL

WORDS AND MUSIC BY JAMIE HOUSTON

Moderately

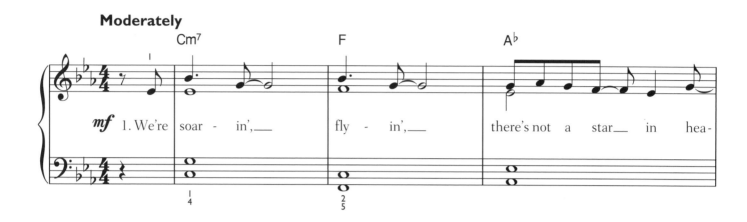

1. We're soar - in', fly - in', there's not a star in hea-

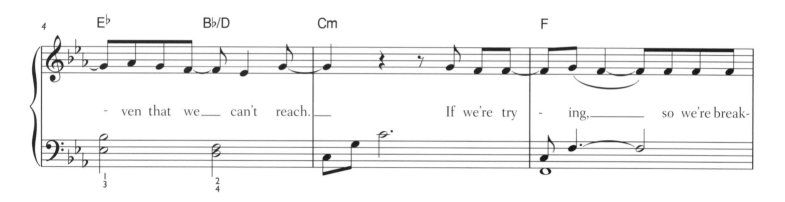

- ven that we__ can't reach.__ If we're try - ing,__ so we're break-

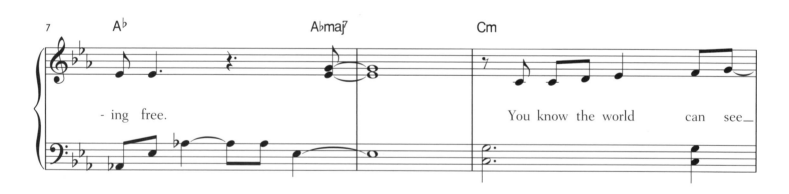

- ing free. You know the world can see__

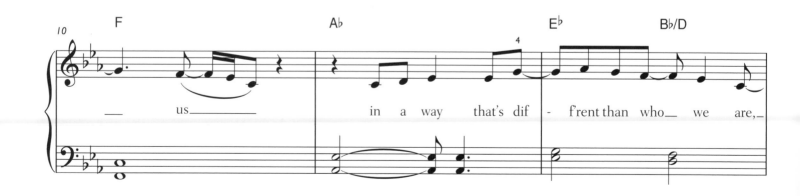

__ us__ in a way that's dif - f'rent than who__ we are,__

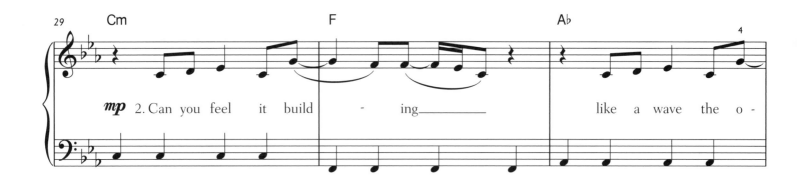

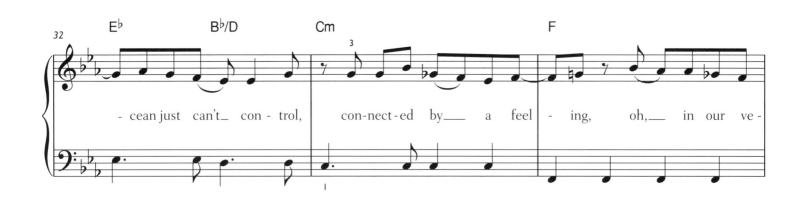

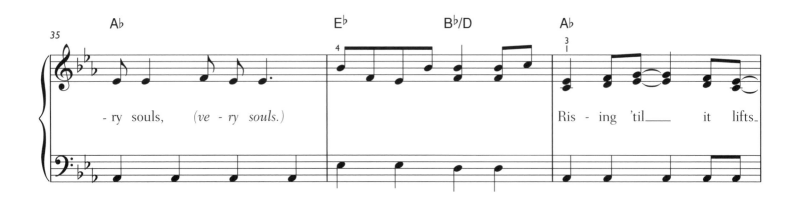

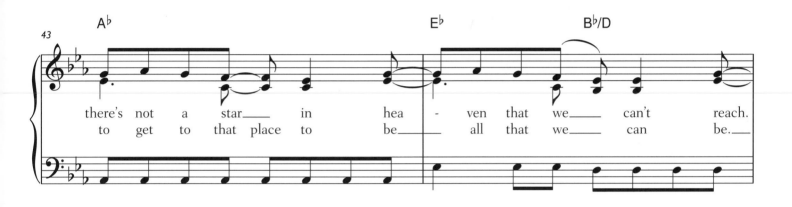

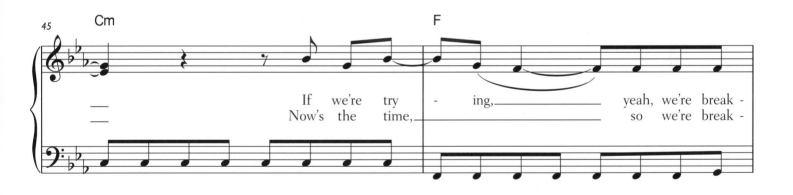

MAYBE THIS TIME

CABARET

WORDS BY FRED EBB
MUSIC BY JOHN KANDER

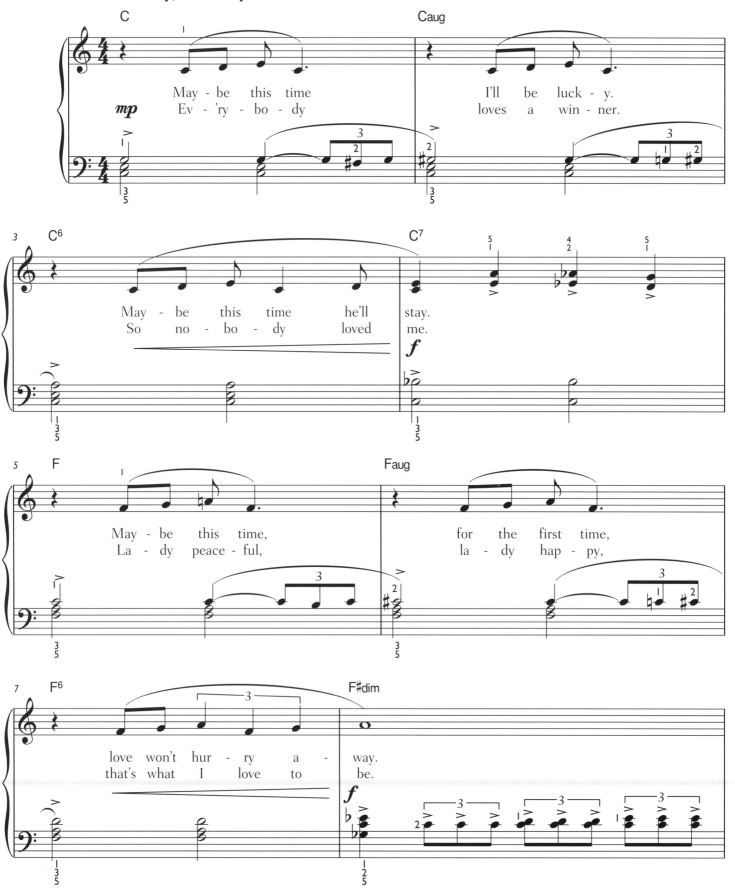

Forcefully, and fairly slow

May - be this time I'll be luck - y.
Ev - 'ry - bo - dy loves a win - ner.

May - be this time he'll stay.
So no - bo - dy loved me.

May - be this time, for the first time,
La - dy peace - ful, la - dy hap - py,

love won't hur - ry a - way.
that's what I love to be.

MEMORY
CATS

MUSIC BY ANDREW LLOYD WEBBER
TEXT BY TREVOR NUNN AFTER T S ELIOT

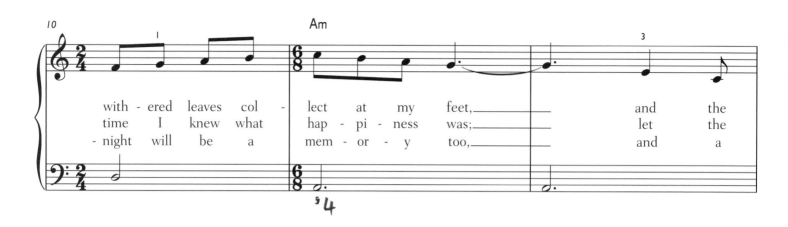

with - ered leaves col - lect at my feet,_____ and the
time I knew what hap - pi - ness was;_____ let the
- night will be a mem - or - y too,_____ and a

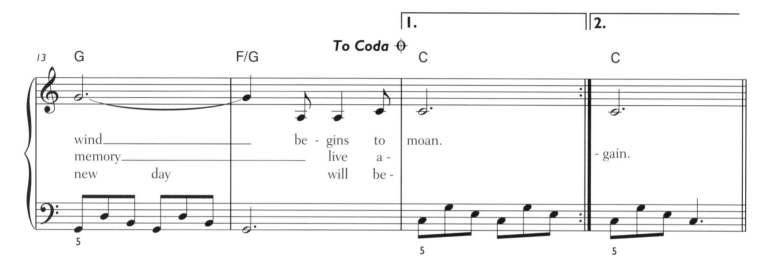

wind_____ be - gins to moan.
memory_____ live a - - gain.
new day will be -

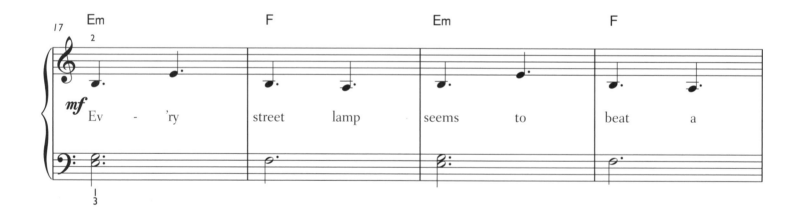

Ev - 'ry street lamp seems to beat a

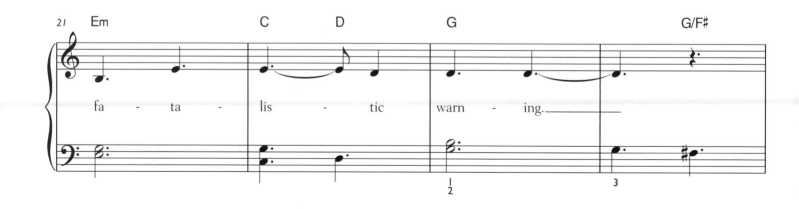

fa - ta - lis - tic warn - ing._____

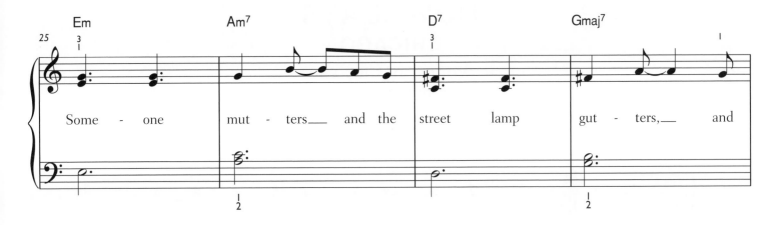

Some - one mut - ters___ and the street lamp gut - ters,___ and

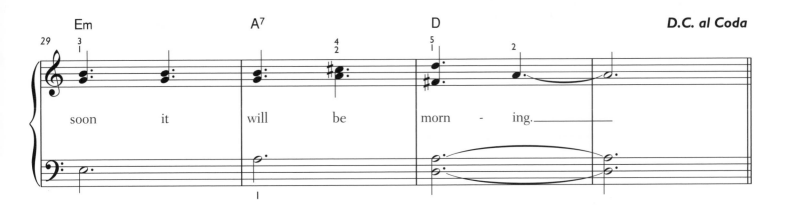

D.C. al Coda

soon it will be morn - ing.___

Coda

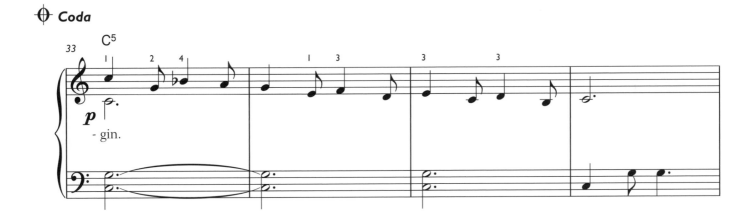

- gin.

rit.

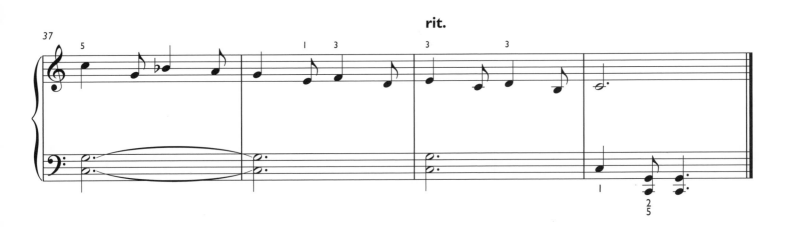

NOWADAYS

CHICAGO

WORDS BY FRED EBB
MUSIC BY JOHN KANDER

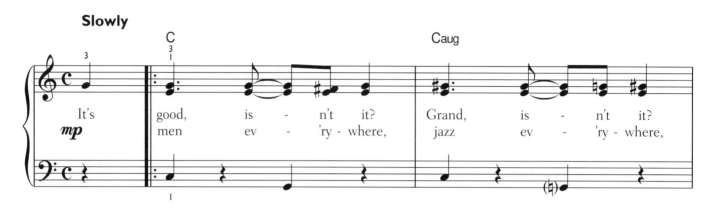

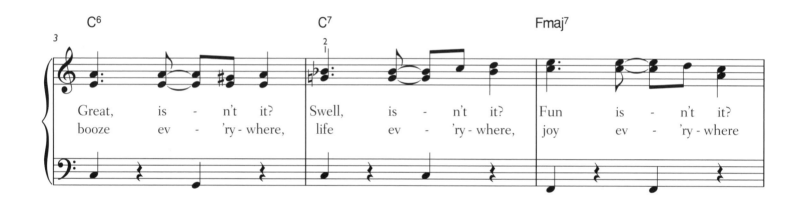

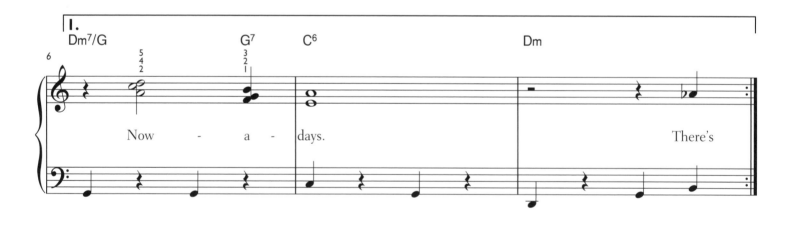

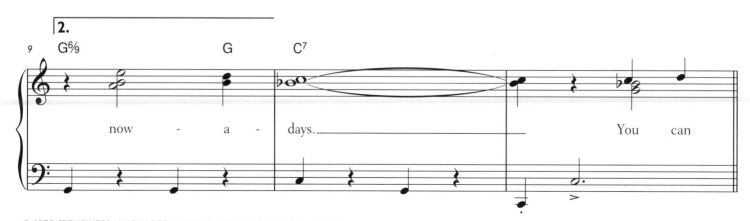

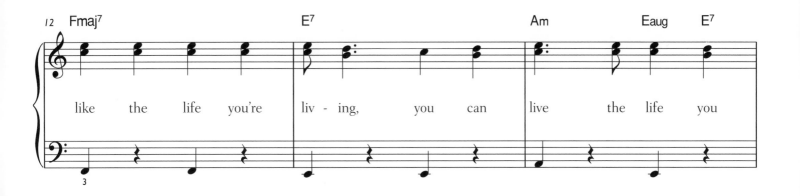

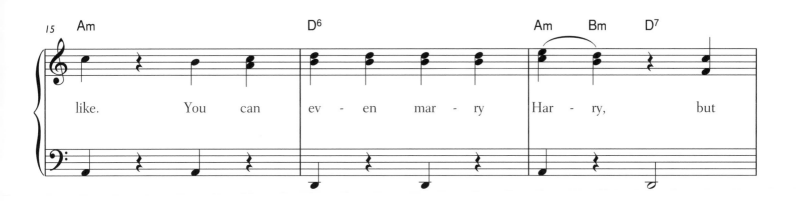

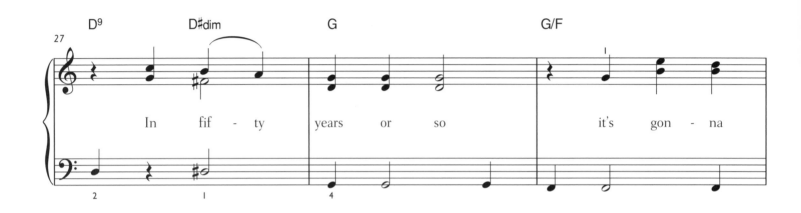

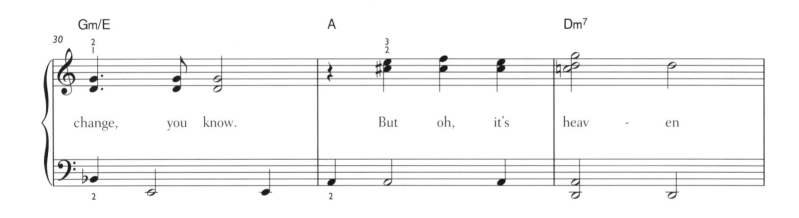

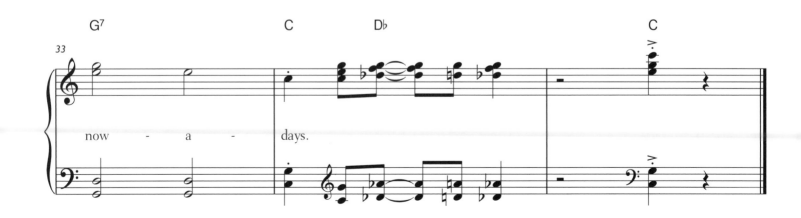

ON THE STREET WHERE YOU LIVE
MY FAIR LADY

WORDS BY ALAN JAY LERNER
MUSIC BY FREDERICK LOEWE

Moderately, in 2

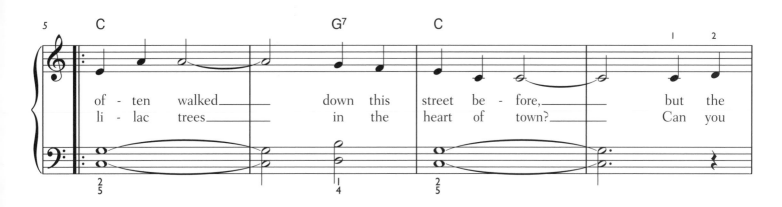

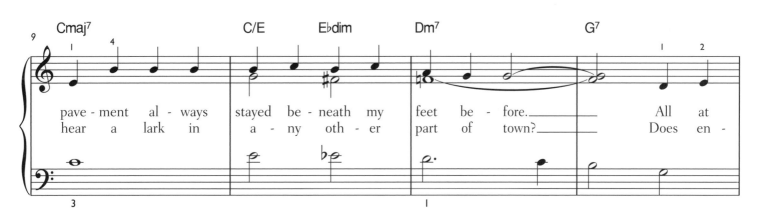

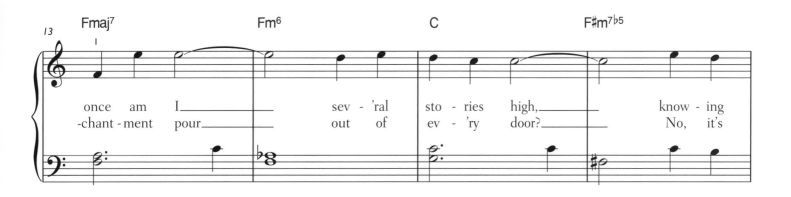

SOMEONE TO WATCH OVER ME
OH, KAY!

MUSIC AND LYRICS BY GEORGE GERSHWIN AND IRA GERSHWIN

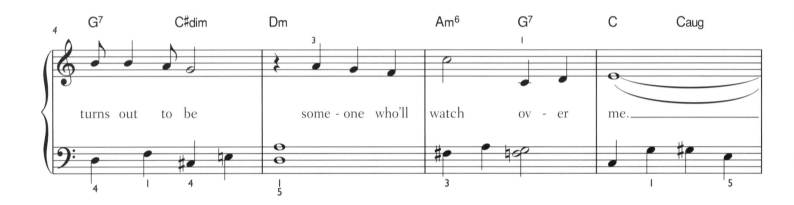

SUMMER NIGHTS
GREASE

WORDS AND MUSIC BY JIM JACOBS AND WARREN CASEY

Moderate rock

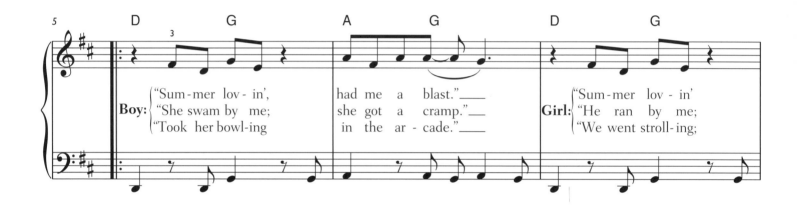

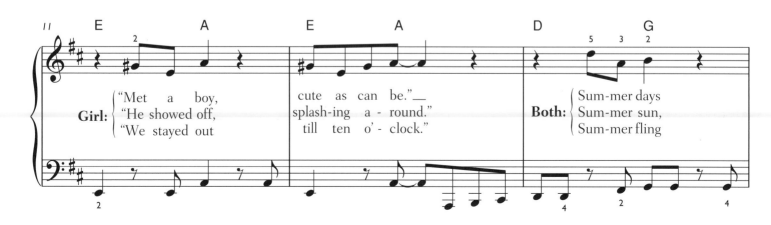

SUMMERTIME
PORGY AND BESS

MUSIC AND LYRICS BY GEORGE GERSHWIN, DU BOSE AND DOROTHY HEYWARD AND IRA GERSHWIN

TOMORROW

ANNIE

WORDS BY MARTIN CHARNIN
MUSIC BY CHARLES STROUSE

Moderately slow

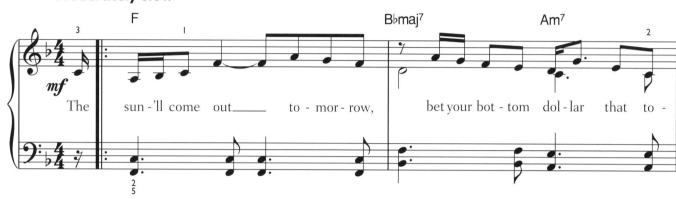

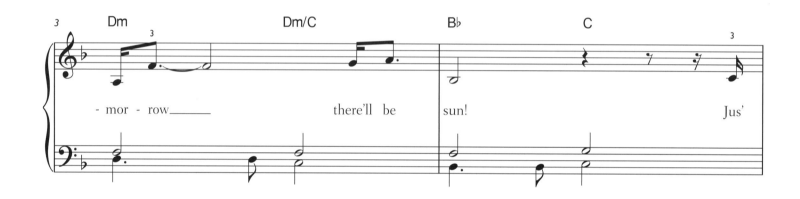

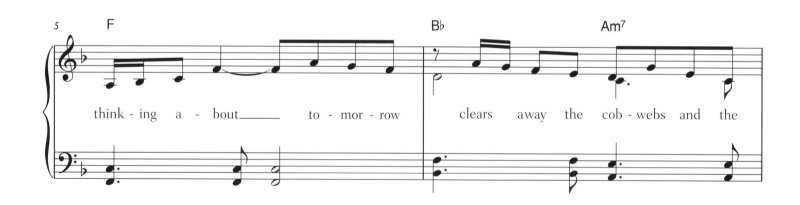

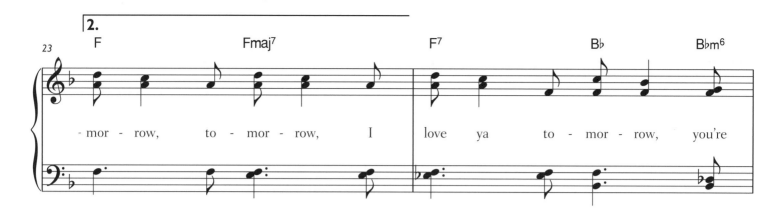

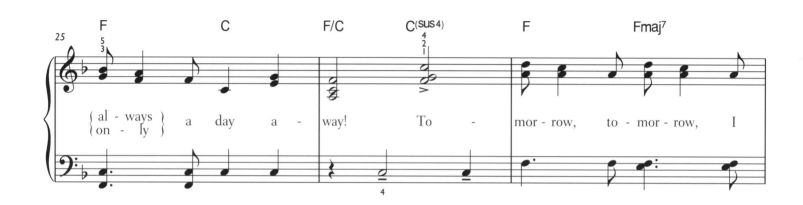

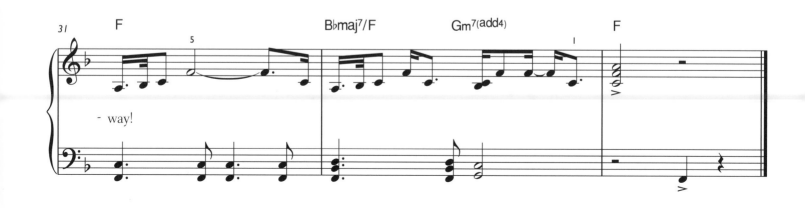

YOU GIVE A LITTLE LOVE
BUGSY MALONE

WORDS AND MUSIC BY PAUL WILLIAMS

We could-'ve been a-ny-thing that we

want-ed to be___ and it's not too late to change.___

I'd be de-light-ed to give it some thought.

May-be you'll a-gree___ that we real-ly ought.

WAIT FOR IT
HAMILTON

WORDS AND MUSIC BY LIN-MANUEL MIRANDA
ARRANGED BY LIN-MANUEL MIRANDA AND ALEX LACAMOIRE

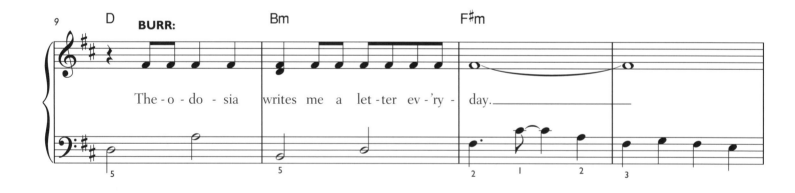

_____ there's a rea - son I'm _____ by her side when so _____ man - y have tried

then I'm _____ will - ing to wait for it. I'm _____ will - ing to

wait for it. (Wait for it, wait for it, wait for it.) My grand - fa - ther was a fire and brim - stone

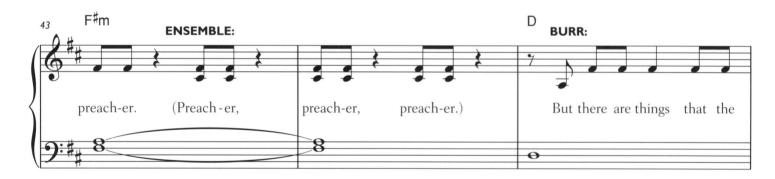

ENSEMBLE: **BURR:**

preach-er. (Preach-er, preach-er, preach-er.) But there are things that the

ENSEMBLE:

hom - i - lies and hymns won't teach ya. (Teach ya, teach ya, teach ya.)

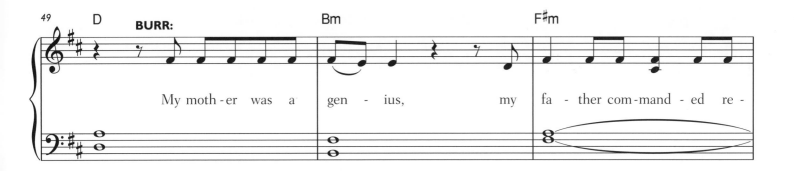

My moth-er was a gen-ius, my fa-ther com-mand-ed re-

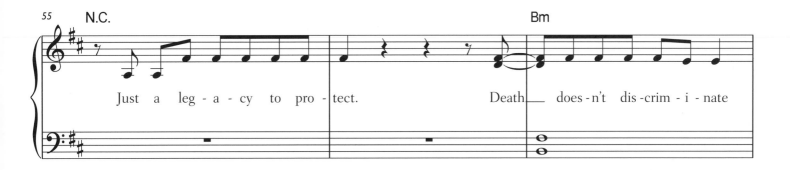

-spect. (Re-spect, re-spect.) When they died they left no in-struc-tions.

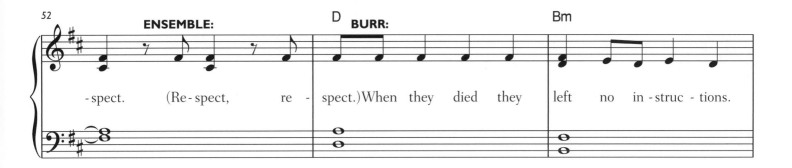

Just a leg-a-cy to pro-tect. Death____ does-n't dis-crim-i-nate

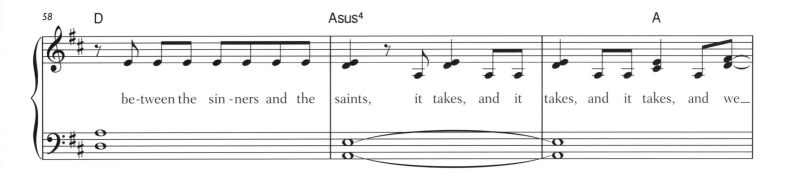

be-tween the sin-ners and the saints, it takes, and it takes, and it takes, and we____

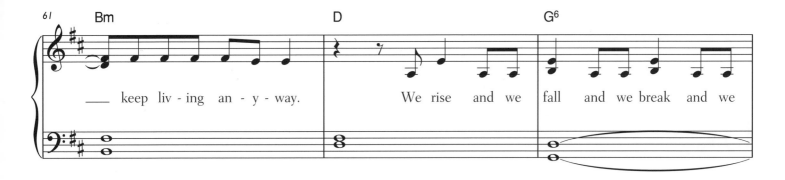

____ keep liv-ing an-y-way. We rise and we fall and we break and we

make our mis-takes. And if____ there's a rea - son I'm____ still a - live when so__

____ man-y have died, then I'm___ will-ing to...

ENSEMBLE: **BURR:** **ENSEMBLE:**

Wait for it...Wait for it...Wait for it... Wait for it...Wait for it...Wait

for it...Wait for it...Wait for it...Wait for it...Wait for it...Wait for it... Wait...

WHERE IS LOVE?
OLIVER!

WORDS AND MUSIC BY LIONEL BART

Slowly

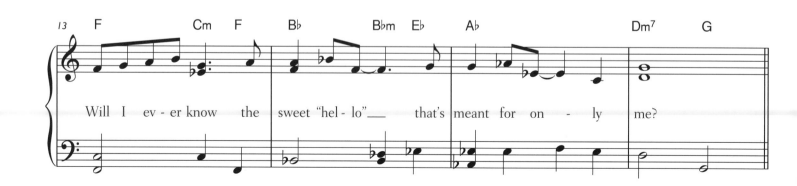

Who can say where she may hide?
Ev-'ry night I kneel and pray,

Must I trav-el far and wide
let to-mor-row be the day

till I am be-side the
when I see the face of

some-one who__

I can mean

some-thing to?__

Where,_____ where_____ is love?

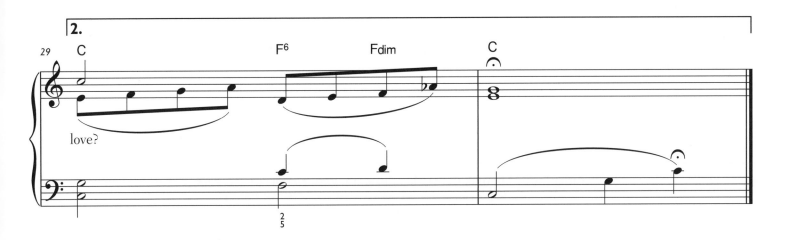

love?

Edited by Lucy Holliday
Designed by Kenosha

© 2018 by Faber Music Ltd
First published by Faber Music Ltd in 2018
Bloomsbury House
74 –77 Great Russell Street
London WC1B 3DA

Printed in England by Caligraving Ltd
All rights reserved

This paper is 100% recyclable

ISBN: 0-571-54033-3
EAN: 978-0-571-54033-4

To buy Faber Music publications or to find out about the full range of titles available,
please contact your local music retailer or Faber Music sales enquiries:

Faber Music Limited, Burnt Mill, Elizabeth Way, Harlow CM20 2HX
Tel: +44 (0)1279 82 89 82   Fax: +44 (0)1279 82 89 83
sales@fabermusic.com   fabermusicstore.com